the secret of happiness ™

GREG S. REID

The Secret of Happiness™
Greg S. Reid

Copyright © 2023

ISBN-13: 978-1-960583-64-2 print edition
ISBN-13: 978-1-960583-65-9 e-book edition

Waterside Productions
2055 Oxford Ave
Cardiff, CA 92007
www.waterside.com

IN APPRECIATION

Special thanks go to our exclusive Happiness Mastermind, who contributed ideas and story direction, as well as insights along our two-year journey. These people have left an indelible mark in the world of personal development and should be acknowledged for such.

Angelika Ullsperger

Oscar Silva

Eric Power

Felipe Manriquez

Gary MacDermind

Lisa Williams

Nadia Linda Hole

Mary-Frances Buckland

Sophia Olivas

A special shout out to those who believed in the journey when we first began: Jasmine Zhang, Theresa Goss, Billy Siordia, and Morgan Rudnick.

CHAPTER ONE

W inter, with its shorter days and lack of sunshine, had never been Hailey's favorite time of year. Her mood always seemed to mirror the gray, overcast skies as each day melted into the next, and those days turned into weeks, and weeks turned into long months. The warm return of spring seemed like an eternity, and now she had to admit that even the promise of sunny days didn't brighten her spirit, like it used to.

This particular Monday was the perfect example, as she prepared to start her work week as a marketing assistant. A cold drizzle had been falling that morning when she left her apartment, which she'd won in a messy divorce battle that went on for more rounds than a championship fight. She almost gave in because her heart couldn't take another round.

The small consulting firm had hired her a couple of years before, and she gladly accepted the position. She saw it as a steppingstone to a promising career, considering she was a stay-at-home wife for most of her adult life.

The owners had assured her that their business was booming. They said that she would receive more opportunities to learn and grow with them than if she was at a larger firm, where she'd have more competition and would likely be at the bottom of the totem pole.

From day one, Hailey had thrown herself into the job, asking questions at every turn and volunteering for the most mundane, and sometimes most difficult, tasks. While it wasn't exactly her dream job, the pay was good, and being a newbie was even better than she'd expected. She was surprised she was given the job considering her resume was sparse, and the only marketing experience she'd had at the time of being hired was her college internship with a not-for-profit organization.

After two years, Hailey had built strong and meaningful relationships within the company and considered herself to be part of the work "family."

As a member of the team, she had always believed she was in the know, so it came as a shock when the owners called a meeting that morning, announcing that business had come upon hard times.

Although they had tried to remain afloat, there was no option but to close their doors.

Walking the twelve blocks back to her newly renovated apartment building, Hailey noticed that even though the rain had stopped, she felt gloomier than she had earlier.

When she'd left that morning, she had a job and an income. Now, she had two weeks' severance pay and unemployment compensation, benefits of which the owners had reminded their employees about, as if that would make everything better.

Far from it, she thought, as she walked through her apartment building's open doors, past JB, the middle-aged doorman. They must have assigned him as a new amenity to the reopened structure.

"Good afternoon, Ms. Hailey," he greeted her with his usual smile.

"Huh? Oh, hi, JB," she replied without returning a smile.

While most days she was happy to engage in small talk with the doorman, today was definitely not one of them.

Entering the mailroom, she unlocked her mailbox and sighed as she pulled out her monthly credit card bill and an envelope from Jackson Barrett Enterprises, the company that owned the 18-floor apartment building.

Must be the new lease transferred to my own name, she thought, considering that she'd moved back into the building right after it reopened.

At the time, she considered herself lucky to earn enough to afford (on her own) an apartment in the newer high rise in a neighborhood that catered to young adults like her.

Her previous salary wasn't impressive by any means, but with a few small sacrifices, she was able to afford the slightly higher rent. This afforded her safety and security, amid a growing waiting list of applicants who wanted to live in a desirable neighborhood, including her former husband.

It wasn't until later that evening that she opened the envelope and was faced with a double whammy. It was a three-month notice that her rent would be increasing "due to rising costs, maintenance, and personnel fees." She felt a sinking feeling wash over her.

The next morning, she took a deep breath before revisiting the events of the previous day and glanced at the notice one more time.

Talk about kicking me when I'm down! What else could go wrong? she muttered out loud.

Frustrated, she pulled her wavy brown hair into a messy ponytail and slung her bag over her shoulder. With nowhere else to go, she grabbed her things and headed to the gym.

Once again, she was greeted by JB on the ground floor.

"Good morning! It looks like today is going to be a beautiful day," he announced.

Hailey's immediate instinct was to shoot back a not-so-happy response, but she stopped herself, realizing that bringing JB down wouldn't help anything.

"I guess," was all she could muster up.

"Is there a problem, Ms. Hailey? Anything I can help you with?" he asked.

Hailey felt a pang of admiration for the doorman, who probably had a lower income than all the tenants in the building, but always acted like he didn't have a care in the world. He seemed to genuinely like his job and every person he interacted with. He also had an amazing reputation for going out of his way to assist anyone who needed it.

He who has less is often the one who has the most.

It was a phrase her dear late grandfather had used often, and although Hailey never gave it much thought or attention, she now knew it was true. JB was living proof.

For the first time, Hailey took a brief interest in him, casting her own challenges aside, wondering if he had a family, where he lived, and what his life was like.

Then, remembering that he had posed a question, she brought herself back to the conversation.

"Thank you, JB, but there's nothing you can do. I'm not sure there is anything anyone can do, to be honest," she sighed. "My company closed its doors yesterday, so it looks like I'm going to have to find a new job, or a less expensive apartment...or win the lottery!"

"Oh, that's too bad," JB responded, before adding his optimism. "I'm sure something will come along soon.

Have you checked the community bulletin board in the mailroom? Maybe something there might interest you."

"I've never checked it out," she admitted. "There are job postings on it?"

"Sometimes. People post all kinds of stuff on there; you never know what you're going to find," he replied.

Then, he reached inside the breast pocket of his impeccable uniform jacket and pulled out a neatly folded section of the daily newspaper.

"In the meantime, help yourself to this," he said, handing it to her.

"Thank you, JB," Hailey said, touched by his generosity.

"My pleasure," he nodded with a smile as he tipped his hat and held the doors open for her.

As she turned her head to thank him once again, she paused to ask him a pressing question.

"JB, how do you do it?"

"Do what?" he asked.

"Stay so happy and upbeat all the time? There's always a smile on your face, and I've never once heard you complain," she noted.

"It's easy, Ms. Hailey, once you know what makes you happy! You see, happiness is a choice, and once you find what makes you happy, you can choose to be happy all the time."

"That's the hard part, JB…finding what makes me happy. How do I do that? It's like a secret that nobody ever shares," she said.

"I assure you that happiness is not a secret," the doorman responded.

"Then what is happiness? If I don't know what it is, how will I ever know that I've found it?" she asked.

"I can't tell you what your *secret of happiness is*, only you can answer that. But I can assure you that you'll know once you find it. It'll happen. You'll see."

His words were backed up with a somewhat mysterious yet knowing smile.

Just what does he know that I don't? Hailey wondered as she walked down the block. She was so distracted by her thoughts; she was unaware that her earlier frustration had been replaced by a small smile. As she glanced at the writing on a small billboard advertisement promoting a local comedy club, her smile grew wider…

"People are about as happy as they make up their minds to be." Abe Lincoln.

Well, what do you know? she audibly laughed aloud. *It must be a sign.*

CHAPTER TWO

A fter spending an hour taking her frustration out on a treadmill and a couple of weight machines at the gym, Hailey grabbed a clean white towel and wiped down the equipment. She'd always been a rule follower; while there were others who believed that it was the staff's responsibility to maintain the center, she didn't mind doing her part at all. After all, it only took a couple minutes … and time was something that she had plenty of right now.

Returning to her apartment, she admired the brick sidewalks that brought a vintage feel to the community, which contrasted nicely with the renovated storefronts. This unique design appealed to the locals walking their dogs, young couples pushing strollers, and shoppers carrying an array of bags from trendy boutiques. Her heart suddenly felt heavy.

I love this neighborhood so much, Hailey thought. *I wish I didn't have to leave.* The irony that she'd fought to keep her apartment in the divorce only to have to give it up just a few months later wasn't lost on her.

It was a thought that had been recurring frequently, and every time it brought with it regret.

"Good morning, Ms. Hailey," JB greeted her as he held the door open wide. "And how was your workout this glorious morning?"

"My workout was just fine, thank you. Trying to take advantage of my membership while I still have it, since I won't be able to afford to renew it. The hits keep coming. You know how it is," she replied.

"I'm sure something will come up, Ms. Hailey," the doorman assured her with a smile that crinkled the corners of his eyes. "That reminds me, did you have a chance to check out the community bulletin board yet?"

"No, I haven't," she admitted, feeling a little guilty. After all, JB was doing his best to try to help her. "I'll do that right away, and thanks again for the help. Looking for another job is the only thing on my agenda this afternoon."

"Then I wish you happy hunting!" he said before swiping his card to let her into the private mailroom.

As she flipped through her mail, she was relieved to see nothing but junk mail. But as she shuffled through the contents, something fell out and dropped to the floor. She looked down to find a black vinyl rectangle at her feet. Curious, she picked it up and turned it over, revealing a sunny yellow magnet that stated nothing more than: "Happy for No Reason."

What is this? she wondered. She peered into her mailbox once again to see if there was a note or anything to indicate where the magnet had come from.

That's strange, she thought when she found nothing that identified the sender. *I wonder what this is about...*

With no answers, she tucked the magnet and her mail into her bag and turned to leave. As she reached the door, she spotted the bulletin board JB had told her about and remembered that she'd promised to check it out.

Among the half dozen notices pinned to the board, was someone seeking a dog walker twice a day, a manicurist's business card, and a few index cards listing items for sale, including a cedar chest and a set of pickleball racquets. The last item was an announcement of a yoga workshop. This caught her interest, so she took a closer look. She was surprised to see it was going to be held the next week, in the apartment building's basement community room. The workshop was focused on stress reduction and would be followed with a presentation by: "Harry Jim, our featured guest speaker."

Now this is new, she thought. *The management has never offered anything like this before. Or did they?*

Curious, she tore off one of the tabs that contained the information to: "Reserve your seat today!" and tucked it into her purse alongside the magnet that someone somewhere had sent her.

"Did you find any employment notices, Ms. Hailey?" JB asked when she returned to the lobby.

"Not really, but I did see an announcement for a yoga workshop that I'm interested in. I think I'm going to register for it," she said.

"Oh? Good. I hope you enjoy it," he said as he pushed the button for the elevator that would take her to her apartment on the seventh floor.

After kicking off her shoes, Hailey slapped the magnet on her refrigerator without giving it a second thought. She made her way to the living room and slumped onto her sofa. She opened the apartment app on her phone and signed up for the workshop.

***

The workshop was held on a Saturday afternoon. Hailey was surprised that the turnout was so great, they had to turn away latecomers. After an hour of yoga and destressing exercises, Harry Jim, the guest speaker walked to the front of the room. He was an eclectic man, adorned with various bracelets, necklaces and rings. His long hair cascaded over his flowing bohemian tunic and denim jeans, exuding a free spirit.

Harry explained how his teaching methods were based on his Hawaiian roots, through breathing techniques that reduced stress, increased wellness, and promoted happiness. When he said, "Happiness is as accessible as the air we breathe," Hailey's interest piqued.

"The breathing technique that will transfer you from your headspace to your heartspace is Aloha," he explained. "You want to start from your core support - your lungs. A lot of us live our lives wanting more, feeling like we don't have enough, and we're always searching for the best way to fill the void we've created. The one thing you have enough of is oxygen. It is always at your disposal and to be happy, you must have oxygen. It is the breath of life."

"Aloha," he said calmly, inhaling deeply and fully, encouraging his audience to do the same. "Aloha means that the breath of God is in our presence. I know you've been told that Aloha is a milkshake at McDonalds, or a communication method Hawaiians use, but it's much deeper than that. It is a powerful force connecting us to the universe. Do you know that being kind, compassionate, loving, and grateful, is in your nature? It is who you are. But that cannot be attained unless you get enough oxygen."

Wait a minute! Hailey thought. *Is Harry telling us that the secret of happiness is as simple as taking a long drink of much-needed air?*

Before she could ponder his claim any further, he continued.

"When I was a kid, people would ask me why I was so happy all of the time, and I said it was because I slept all day … that and I had a surfboard," he laughed.

"Breathing at that pace makes you happy. Sleeping makes you fulfilled. If you're happy enough, that means you're breathing enough."

For Hailey, the connection was forming. After all, in the past, she'd felt the peace of being in a trouble-free zone before, and practicing his breathing technique reminded her of it.

"Breathing slowly and deeply puts you in a serene state, like you're on the verge of falling into a long, deep sleep. On the flip side, we've also felt exuberant after expanding our lungs during physical activity - something joggers and marathoners refer to as the euphoric feeling of a runner's high. There is a feeling of abundance at these times, a feeling of having enough or, better yet, of having a cup that runs over," Harry advised.

It was apparent that Harry was onto something, and Hailey wanted to learn more.

"The only way to deal with a happy person is to realize that they are off duty. They are not owning another expectation, and they are not feeling victimized," he advised.

Then, Harry revealed his golden nugget.

"If you aren't happy, you can be … and far sooner than you think. Happiness is literally just a breath away! Literally, a breath away," he advised before walking them through a two-minute breathing exercise.

"Stop everything and take a breath right now. Take a long, deep breath.

"Take your next deep breath through your nose," he said, demonstrating the process as he explained.

"Deep, full breaths. Feel those full lungs. Fill them up."

For the next couple minutes, he continued to take deep, exaggerated and intentional breaths of air, inhaling and exhaling fully while sharing his thoughts about the state of happiness.

"Happiness is like someone opened the door and let the air in. It is not in negotiating. It is in navigating to it, and we can do that breath by breath, letting the air guide us directly to our fulfillment.

"Abundance is not something we possess. Abundance belongs to being present in our experiences. What magic it is to understand that! It is not about being on the surfboard; it's about being on your life's platform. This has the capacity to change your life in the moment," Harry advised.

As Hailey felt the tension melt off her shoulders, Harry gave her a sense of optimism.

"I want everyone to consider being contagiously happy, not by structure or form but by breath. I promise that happiness is only two minutes away. If you just give yourself the fullness of breath, you can navigate your problems full sail … and that is the foundation of happiness, no matter what outside forces or challenges you might face," he said.

To Hailey, it was like he was speaking directly to her.

Afterward, Hailey mingled with the attendees, many of which she didn't know, even though they were all residents of the building. When the renovation took place, some of the former residents chose to relocate permanently. Hailey, however, had always been drawn to the neighborhood, and the prospect of living in a renovated apartment sealed the deal. While the renovation was inconvenient, it was temporary, and Hailey never regretted her decision to renew her lease.

This workshop reminded her how little she knew about the other people who occupied the building. For a brief moment, it occurred to her that unless she found a job soon, she might never know them.

A sigh escaped her lips when she walked into her apartment and was once again surprised at its transformation and how much she loved what the designers had done with it. Her eyes swept across the modern kitchen, with its white cabinets and high-end finishes that contrasted perfectly with the brick floors.

Taking a deep breath, she paused to admire her home, like she'd done many times since she had moved back in. This time, something new caught her eye. The plant she'd lovingly placed in the windowsill on the day she moved back in, was blooming for the very first time.

For a split second, she forgot her troubles. She wasn't even aware that she was smiling when she said out loud, "After the winter comes the spring."

CHAPTER THREE

During the next few days, Hailey focused on job searches and updating her resume. It didn't take long to realize that competition in marketing was fierce. She concluded that she needed the assistance of a headhunter if she wanted to get a lucrative position.

So, Hailey contacted an employment agency and made an appointment for the following week.

On the morning of her appointment, she chose her clothes carefully. She wanted to look professional, but not cookie cutter; capable, but creative. After putting her hair up, then down, then up again, a quick glance at her phone told her that she needed to schedule a ride if she didn't want to be late.

Just as she swiped to find the Uber app on her phone, she remembered that the apartment building's app was all inclusive. She could use it to report maintenance issues, contact Security, or order third-party services, like Door Dash and Uber.

This is pretty handy, she thought as she tapped the button and completed her transaction. *It would be nice if the rest of my day went this smoothly.*

Thirty minutes later, she stepped out of the elevator and was greeted by JB.

"Hello, Ms. Hailey," came the friendly greeting she had grown accustomed to. "Allow me to get the door for you."

"That's okay, JB. I'm expecting an Uber, so I'll just wait here for a few. He should be along any minute now," she informed him.

"Very good," JB replied, just as the elevator doors opened once again.

"Good morning, JB," the man who stepped out said.

"It is a good morning, Dr. Wagner," JB smiled as he made his way to the entry doors.

"That's okay, JB. I'm waiting for my Uber," the man said.

"Then I should introduce you, that is, if you don't already know each other," JB advised. "Dr. Wagner, this is Hailey. She's been a tenant for a few years, I believe. Ms. Hailey, this is Dr. Wagner. He's relatively new here. I believe he moved in about the same time that I took this position."

As the two shook hands, a shiny gunmetal gray SUV pulled alongside the curb, in front of the entry doors.

"Here's my ride," Hailey and Dr. Wagner said in unison.

Caught off guard, the two looked at each other in confusion.

A short ring told Hailey that she had a text message, and a quick glance at the screen showed her that her Uber had arrived.

Ding … Dr. Wagner pulled out his phone.

"Yes, my ride is here," he said.

"Wait—I think that's mine," Hailey said. "I just received a notification."

"So did I," Dr. Wagner mentioned, unable to hide his puzzled tone.

"I have an appointment downtown and can't be late," Hailey told him, hoping he'd be willing to wait for another ride.

"I'm going downtown, too. I'd be happy to share the Uber, that is, if that ok with you," Dr. Wagner offered.

"Yes, please," Hailey agreed with a sigh of relief. "I can't afford to be late. I accept!"

Once they settled in the vehicle, Dr. Wagner opened the conversation.

"So, you've been in the apartment building for a few years. Is it much different than it used to be?" he asked.

"It is different, but in the renovation process, they managed to keep all the things I've loved about the building, while making some much-needed improvements. Overall, the renovations made it more appealing." she said. "It's all great, but the raised rent couldn't have come at a worse time."

"Oh?" Dr. Wagner asked, waiting for Hailey to explain.

"Yes, the company I worked for just went out of business. I have an appointment with an employment agency today—that's why I was afraid to be late," Hailey said before turning the conversation to her travel companion.

"JB said you recently moved in. Where did you live before?" she asked.

"I've lived in multiple countries," he advised with a smile. "I lived in Bhutan for three years. Did you know that Bhutan is known for being the happiest country in the world?"

"Really? I didn't know that," Hailey answered. "What's their secret?"

"I believe it started back in 1973, when the Fourth Dragon King of Bhutan made a speech, declaring that gross national happiness is better than the gross national product. It was a very simple, straightforward sentence that evolved into an opportunity to develop gross national happiness in their country. Now, Bhutan is like any other country; they have happy people and sad people. However, they are the only country that tries to quantify the happiness within their nation."

"If they have both happy and sad people, how does that make them the happiest?" Hailey inquired.

"Bhutan's GDP is small, especially when compared with other countries. However, there is not a single person who is starving and living on the streets. They are an agricultural country, and 80 percent of the population lives on their farms and eat what they sow. Their citizens do not have money. According to Western philosophies, their income is sad, but this is not the case at all. The people do not live in lack. They have food. Their healthcare and education are free. In short, they are happy because no one is suffering. While they don't have money, they have enough. That is their sweet spot."W

"What's worth noting is that being the happiest country isn't just their self-appointed title or claim to fame. Their happiness is actually researched. When Bhutan conducts its census, it is accompanied by an extensive survey that was developed to determine their Gross National Happiness index. The answers to that questionnaire drive policy every three years and every ten years. From there, ten-year plan is derived from the results," he shared.

"It sounds like they figured out the secret of happiness," Hailey said. "Do you agree with it?"

"For me, the secret of happiness is feeling like you have enough. For some, that could be enough material possessions, enough knowledge, or enough love. The feeling of impermanence is that everything comes and goes. Therefore, if you don't feel you have enough, you're always chasing something more, and that brings suffering. In my opinion, doesn't matter how much you have; if you feel you don't have enough, you will seek more and happiness will elude you."

"Interesting," Hailey said. "So, Dr. Wagner, what do you do, and does it make you happy?"

"I am a physic teacher," he replied. "I used to be an academic and worked in research. When I look at my field as a physics teacher, I am at the top of my game, and I know that should be enough. I have to check myself when I see a friend who bought a house for a million dollars and remind myself that shouldn't have any impact on me because I never wanted a million-dollar home. I move around the world, and every two years, I'm living in a different place. I am 'just' a teacher, and I love being a teacher. That's enough for me. It's my goal, and it makes me happy. Of course, I always want to be a better teacher, but I am content with what I do and where I am in my life," he shared.

"Hmm, I think that's what I'm looking for now—a job that fulfills me and where I'm happy to settle in for the long term," Hailey said.

"You'll find it, Hailey. Just look for the sweet spot," Dr. Wagner assured her.

"The sweet spot? What's that?" she asked.

"It's the place between striving, succeeding, and growing, while being content and satisfied at the same time. When you find that and embrace it without exception, perhaps that is when, like the residents of Bhutan, you will know that you are the happiest you can be."

His wisdom wasn't lost on Hailey, and after they parted ways and she walked into the employment agency, she found her agenda had changed.

She was no longer looking for a job—any job. Suddenly, she wanted more.

She wanted to find her sweet spot.

CHAPTER FOUR

A lways punctual, it wasn't a surprise for Hailey to find that she had arrived early for her appointment. Hailey checked in with the receptionist, a friendly young woman who reminded her of her optimistic self, many years before. She took a seat in one of the plastic ultra-modern chairs in the waiting room. A quick glance at the clock on the fake-wood wall told her that she had nearly 20 minutes before her scheduled appointment, and Hailey wished that the room had a TV. Listening to a 24-hour news channel wasn't fun, but it beat scrolling through her social media accounts for the tenth time that morning.

She had just talked herself into pulling out her phone when a man in a blue business suit walked into the room and told the receptionist his name.

"Great. Mr. Goodwin is in a meeting and should be out in a few minutes. Please have a seat, and I'll let him know you're here, Mr. Meltzer," she said with a friendly smile.

Hailey watched as the gentleman looked around and approached her.

"Is this seat taken?" he smiled.

"I don't believe so," she answered.

"Good. I'm glad someone else is here to keep me company while I wait. It makes the time pass much more quickly; don't you think?" he asked.

"I guess it does," she replied. Then, seeing his words as an invitation to strike up a conversation, she asked, "What type of job are you looking for?"

"Me? Oh, no, I'm not looking for a job. I'm here to meet with the owner of the agency. My company is planning a fundraiser, and Mr. Goodwin has graciously volunteered to partner with us. We're meeting today to get the ball rolling. How about you? What are you here for today, if I might ask?" he said.

"I'm here looking for a job. I'm meeting with a Ms. Hayden. Do you know her?" Hailey replied.

"No, I can't say that I do. But I don't know you, either," he said. "My name is David Meltzer. And you are...?"

"Hailey," she smiled. "My name is Hailey."

"What type of job are you looking for, Hailey?" he asked.

"Well, I have a marketing background, so that would probably be the best fit. But I'm currently unemployed, so I'm open to other opportunities. On the other hand, I've just recently realized that I want a career that offers more than an income. I'm looking for something fulfilling, but definitely not temporary. My dream job would open the door to a long-term career. That's what would make me happy. Am I asking too much?"

"Absolutely not!" David declared. "That's not too much to ask for ... and it's not that difficult to find."

"Really?" she questioned.

"Really," he repeated. "The best way for anyone to get what they want, whether it's a job or anything else that will make them happy, is by being grateful."

"Even if we all want totally different things?" she asked.

"Yes. We do all want different things, and different things make different people happy. For one person, the secret might be to bask in the sunshine all day, every day, while another might state that the real secret of happiness is to be barefoot jumping in puddles and singing in the rain. This draws the conclusion that success and happiness can be as individual and unique to every person as their fingerprint. But while we're all different, I've found that happiness is the only common denominator of gracious people, meaning that happiness and gratitude are intertwined in each other. It doesn't matter how tall or short you are, no matter what religion you are, no matter how much money you have or don't have, or no matter how sick or heathy you are, gratitude is happiness," he said.

Listening to him, Hailey became intrigued with his perspective and was excited to have him elaborate.

"Tell me more about how gratitude works," she encouraged.

"People tell me I've changed their life by telling them to say thank you before they go to bed and when they wake up for 30 straight days. I suggest you try it, as well. But I've learned that coherence needs to be attached to happiness. That means to remember to be happy and do it. Remember to say thank you and do it. Why is it that it takes 1/10th of a second and it's free to say thank you, but everyone forgets to say thank you or they don't say it at all, even though they can't argue the power in doing so?" he posed, pausing for her response.

"Hmm, that's a good question," she said.

"Just saying thank you *will* change your life, Hailey. Every thought leader in the world has some sort of gratitude challenge or journal. The metaphysics, quantum physics, and physics will tell you how powerful gratitude is. But gratitude really is perception—the ability to find the light, the love, and lesson in everything. Then you have to determine if it feeds you or bleeds you. Determine if it is worth your time to find it, live with it, or change it."

"I'm intrigued. Can you tell me how the process actually works?" Hailey asked.

"I believe happiness is a relationship between two speeds: the speed of light, which is the time that the particle of light leaves the sun, and the speed of thought. Those who think that happiness is derived from within, are correct. Those who can derive happiness outside of themselves, are correct. But there is a connection between the two, and you can have either, or most importantly and hopefully, both."

"I hear you, but lately happiness doesn't seem attainable, at least not right away," Hailey admitted.

"I think when you believe there is an all-powerful, all-knowing source that loves you the way a mother loves her child, happiness is not a moving target. The real question is what are you doing to interfere with your happiness and not doing to become happy?" he explained.

"Wait, you're saying that I'm actually stopping myself from being happy? That doesn't make sense. Of course, I don't want to be unhappy. Nobody does," she replied.

"Remember, Hailey, there is ease and dis-ease. We want to figure out what we are doing that is putting us at dis-ease. Thoughts come first, so those people who work in the ego, the need to be right, superior, offended, separate, anxious, frustrated, or angry, are not going to be happy. They are putting themselves at dis-ease."

Given that his responses were fascinating, Hailey encouraged David to continue.

"A lot of people say money cannot buy happiness. I say money does not buy happiness, but it allows you to shop, and if you shop for the right things for the right reasons, you'll be happy. Let me give you an example. I always tell people not to buy a Ferrari. Hey, I know—I bought one, and it caused me a lot of problems. Then one day, I met one of the inner-city kids that I coach, and he had bought a Lamborghini. I was disappointed and asked him why he bought it. He said, 'When kids come up to me and ask me how I got this car—am I a rapper, a basketball player, or an entertainer—I tell them no. I read books, and I help people.' Now that's a great reason to buy something, and it makes him happy."

"I bet it does. That is a great story," Hailey smiled.

"It is, isn't it? It also supports the theory that doing something for others can increase our own happiness. That's why I'm doing this fundraiser. It makes me happy. But let's turn the tables back to you. What about those pauses in time when unhappiness sets in? Do those emotions and experiences make us even more grateful for the happiness we do experience? I say that we need to identify moments of unhappiness when it sets in, so we can put them to rest. It's like your mother taught you to do when there is a fire: stop, drop, and roll. Stop, breathe in, and breathe out. Drop the negative thoughts, and then move past them."

"You're saying we can actually stop and make a choice to be happy, rather than unhappy?" Hailey asked.

"Happiness is a choice, and unhappiness is a choice, as well. Absolutely! A lot of people put their attention and intention on the coincidences they don't want and what's missing or what other people want for them. That's what makes them unhappy. You can absolutely change that and put your attention and intention on what makes *you* happy," Mr. Meltzer stated.

"Hailey, every day is a reset. You're given 24 hours of activity every day. It's so important to have what I call 'new day resolutions.' You can start over at any time. Utilizing your time to do what you want is an absolute refresh. Reset every day. What you thought or believed yesterday might not be so today. After all, you're always changing, growing, and learning," he advised.

"I think this is just what I needed to hear. Thank you, David. Can I ask you a personal question?"

"Sure, go ahead," David responded.

"What does happiness mean to you?" she asked.

"My definition of happiness is to be able to enjoy the everyday, consistent, persistent pursuit of your own potential—not what other people want, but what *you* want. And remember, there is no pursuit of happiness; happiness *is* the pursuit! Like I said, it all stems from gratitude and giving someone else something to be grateful for, as well. I like to say that happiness is planting seeds under trees you may never sit under," he said.

"That's profound. I'll have to remember that saying," she said, nodding her head in agreement.

Just then, the receptionist called her name, announcing that Ms. Hayden was ready for their meeting.

"Thank you, David," Hailey said. "I enjoyed our conversation very much."

"So did I. Here, let me give you my business card. Let me know if you want to continue our talk or if there is any way I can help you in your endeavors," he said, passing her his card.

As she walked away, Hailey glanced at David Meltzer's card and suddenly realized that there was something behind it. Lifting it up, she noted that another card was stuck to the back of it. Flipping it over, she was surprised at what it said: "Happy for no reason!"

That's strange, she thought as the receptionist escorted her down the hall. *I've never seen this before, but now I've received it not once, but twice. Is somebody trying to tell me something? If so, who?*

CHAPTER FIVE

O nce the meeting was over, Hailey felt disappointed. She wasn't expecting to walk out the door with shining job prospects in hand, but she also wasn't expecting to feel like she hadn't made any progress at all.

The job recruiter, Ms. Hayden, hadn't discussed any job openings with her at all. Instead, she provided an overview of their services and, yes, their fees. She perused Hailey's current resume and made a few suggestions that could make it more appealing to prospective employers. And she gave Hailey a homework assignment, passing her a brochure with the login information to take a career assessment.

"Now, don't get anxious about it. It's relatively painless. Just some questions that will help us determine the best fit for your experience and personality," the woman smiled. "We find that skills by themselves aren't the best determining factors in placements or referrals. But when you combine skills with interests, values, and character traits, that will help us find the best employer for an applicant and the best applicant for an employer."

"Thank you. I will be sure to take the assessment right away. In the meantime, if any openings come up that I'm qualified for, please do not hesitate to contact me. I'm ready to get back to work as soon as I can," Hailey replied.

Realizing that the likelihood of a paycheck in the near future was slim, at best, Hailey opted to take the bus home. *It might not be as nice as an Uber*, she thought, *but it won't cost as much.*

The city buses had recently undergone a facelift. Over the course of the past few months, she had noticed that the busses had been wrapped. Some promoted local businesses or health services. Having businesses pay to advertise on the city's busses helped defray costs and reduce prices for the passengers. Other busses had wraps that promoted the city and their services. It gave a fresh look to the vehicles, Hailey thought, as she sat on a bench waiting for the bus that would take her home to the west side.

The wait gave her a chance to mull over taking the assessment. She'd never taken one before and didn't know what to expect. As she thought about it, she began to worry. What if she answered something wrong? What if she didn't know the answers to some of the questions? She couldn't help but notice the anxiety creeping in. This is exactly what Ms. Hayden told her not to worry about. Harry Jim's breathing advice popped into her mind, and she took a deep breath.

By the time the bus pulled up, she felt better. Briefly noticing that this particular bus boasted a Chamber of Commerce advertisement, she climbed aboard, glad to see that there was plenty of room. Opting to sit by herself, she chose an empty seat across from a man who had a guitar perched on the vinyl seat beside him.

"Hello," he smiled. "Beautiful day, isn't it?"

"Yes, it is," Hailey agreed. Then, trying to be polite, she gave a nod to his guitar. "I take it you play?"

"I sure do. I'll play anytime, anywhere. Whatever I can do to earn a few bucks and get a paying gig," he said.

"Really? What kind of music do you play?" Hailey asked, genuinely interested.

"Whatever makes people happy," the man said.

"Which song makes your fans happiest?" she asked.

"Oh, yes, there is one that always gets the crowd going," he answered, reaching for his guitar. "Do you want to hear it?"

Uncertain, Hailey looked around the bus, wondering what the other passengers would think if this guy broke out his guitar and started singing. Reading her uncertainty, the man spoke up.

"Everybody okay with it if I play a little tune and entertain y'all on the ride?" he asked.

After hearing a few sures, okays, and even one "hell yes!", he strummed a few chords, and then provided a brief intro into the song.

"This song is one of my favorites because it's got such a great vibe. It's a number called Build Me Up, Buttercup. Maybe you'll recognize it," he smiled.

> Why do you build me up Buttercup, baby
> Just to let me down and mess me around
> And then worst of all you never call, baby

When you say you will (say you will) but I love you still
I need you more than anyone, darlin'
You know that I have from the start
So build me up Buttercup, don't break my heart.
(Written by: Tony Macauley, Mike D'Abo
Lyrics © Universal Music Publishing Group, Warner Chappell Music, Inc.)

Listening to his pleasant voice sing the lyrics to one of the most popular and infectious songs of all time, Hailey couldn't help but smile. He was a great singer who had a knack for relating to his listeners, even from a bus seat. And it wasn't long before she was singing along with the rest of the passengers.

By the time he hit the last verse, the entire bus had joined in, even the bus driver.

I need you more than anyone, baby
You know that I have from the start
So build me up, Buttercup, don't break my heart…

Once the applause subsided, Hailey thanked him.

"Thank you. That really made my day. You're really good, you know that—don't you?" she asked.
"I know that music makes me happy, so it's what I like to do, whether or not I'm good," he explained.

"Where are you playing next? I'd like to come listen to you, if I can," she asked.

"Here, there, you know, anywhere. Actually, I don't have anything lined up right now. It's difficult for people to know who I am without an agent or a website. But that doesn't stop me. I figure if I keep on playing, somebody somewhere will hear me, and my career will take off," he said optimistically.

Suddenly, Hailey had an idea.

"I don't know if I can help, but can I have your name and number? If I hear of anything, I'll be glad to let you know," she volunteered.

As she finished entering his information into her contacts on her phone, the bus pulled up to her stop.

"Thanks again for the entertainment," she smiled. "Keep spreading sunshine!"

As she watched the bus drive away, she noticed the quote printed on its side.

> *"A pessimist sees the difficulty in every opportunity;*
> *an optimist sees the opportunity in every difficulty."*
> – Winston Churchill

Interesting, she thought as she walked toward her apartment building. Suddenly aware that she was still smiling, she realized that she actually felt happy. Then she realized that she didn't have anything to really be happy about.

What do you know, she thought, *I'm happy for no reason. Maybe those little reminders that keep coming my way are starting to have an effect on me.*

"Hello, Ms. Hailey," greeted JB when she approached the doorway. "It looks like you're having a good day. Perhaps a promising job prospect?"

"Not yet, JB. But suddenly things are looking up. I think spring is in the air," she grinned.

Inside her apartment, she kicked her pumps off at the door and tossed her purse on the counter. As she grabbed a bottle of water out of the fridge, the plant in the windowsill caught her eye. She pulled it down to give it a drink of water, as well, and admire the color of its blossoms.

What a nice sunny shade of yellow, she thought.

"Like a buttercup," she said out loud to no one but herself. "Imagine that."

With that, she sat on the sofa and opened her laptop. She had work to do. If there was opportunity in every difficulty, it was high time she started looking for it.

CHAPTER SIX

Hailey didn't take the two-hour assessment until the next morning. She had been too busy researching opportunities and possible venues for Weston to turn her attention to anything else.

It wasn't that Weston was a priority over finding employment. She just didn't see that there would be immediate gratification from taking the assessment. At least in believing she was helping someone else, she felt like she was doing something productive.

As a marketer, she had faith that she could help Weston get the exposure he needed. He had the talent, no doubt, and he had what was known as stage presence. He could relate to his audience anywhere, she was sure of that, even if it was on a city bus.

As she scoured local sites for entertainment venues, she came across an announcement that intrigued her. The Chamber of Commerce was sponsoring a street expo and fair, and it was going to be held right there in her neighborhood, which was touted as "rich in character and opportunities."

Oh my gosh! she thought, *this is exciting! Why didn't I know about this before? I absolutely love this idea! I'd give anything to be part of this!*

With that thought, she sent an email to the Chamber of Commerce, introducing herself. She provided a bit of her background and volunteered to help in any way she could. Then, she jotted a quick line at the end: "Is there any entertainment lined up yet? If so, are there any open slots available? I know a local resident who would be awesome!"

***

The next morning, she poured her coffee and logged in to take the assessment. The notice on the screen told her it covered four sections, each containing 50 questions. The assessment would be timed, and she had two hours to complete all 200 questions.

"No anxiety, no pressure … right," she muttered.

Ms. Hayden had been right. The questions were vague and required her to select her response to different hypothetical situations.

There were no right answers. There were no wrong answers. But every answer had the potential to categorize her as analytical, creative, assertive, collaborative … and everything in between.

When she finished the test with a deep sigh two long hours later, a statement appeared, saying the recruiter would send her the results within 48 hours.

For the next hour, she perused job sites, only to find that there had been little change since the last time she'd searched.

"So much for that," she said.

Her thoughts were interrupted by the notification that she'd received an email. To her surprise, she found a reply from the Chamber of Commerce in her inbox. They thanked her for reaching out and stated they welcomed volunteers to assist with the street fair.

"We would love to have you onboard to help in marketing and promoting the event," the email said. "I invite you to stop by the office to learn more about how you can assist us in making this the success we know it can be! And, yes, we are lining up entertainment for the main stage. Vendors and independent artists are also welcome to submit an application, which can be found on our website."

Hailey quickly hopped onto the website to see what Weston needed to do to perform at the fair, only to be disappointed to learn that there was a $200 fee to secure the spot.

I don't think Weston can swing that. He needs someone to pay him to play, not the other way around, she thought.

But all wasn't lost—she'd been invited to stop by and talk to them, so there was still hope. Hitting reply, she returned a quick email stating she'd drop by that afternoon.

She had never visited the Chamber of Commerce before, but she'd passed by it many times. While it was located on the edge of the community she loved, its modern steel and glass storefront seemed out of place next to the cobblestone sidewalk and business doorways framed in carved marble or aged stucco. Hailey supposed the modern architecture was meant to reflect the appeal of high-rise business buildings and the success that filled them, but to her, it fell short.

Still, she was excited about the opportunity to learn more about the fair. It wasn't a paying job, but it was an opportunity to do something new and make new connections … and that couldn't hurt.

Hmm, maybe this is what Winston Churchill meant when he said to find an opportunity in difficulty. And it was easier than I thought it would be! she thought.

***

The meeting went well, and Hailey took a fast liking to Grace, the office manager, and Preston, the current chair of the Chamber. They spent an hour telling her about the schedule and showing her how to answer the phone, log into the computer, but they mostly focused on sponsorship and business participation. With the goal of drawing large crowds for the business owners to cater to, they wanted every business to have an equal opportunity to promote and feature themselves.

"Hailey, we really need someone to reach out to the businesses and encourage their participation. Let them know about opportunities to sponsor the event and how it can benefit them. You can call them, but we find that we get stronger involvement by visiting them in person, so you might have to put in some legwork. Are you up for that?" Preston asked.

"Absolutely! I actually love walking through the community," she assured him. "I'll get started straight away!"

***

The next day, she entered a bistro that she'd been wanting to visit since it opened last summer. Arriving just after they opened, she hoped that would give her an opportunity to speak with the owner before the lunch rush. To her surprise, there were patrons already sitting at most of the tables. So, when the hostess asked her to have a seat for a few minutes while she spoke to the owner, Hailey sat down on one of the stools at the bar.

"Hello," she politely said to the woman sitting next to her.

"Good morning!" the woman replied, pushing the book in front of her to the side. "Here, let me move this so it's not in your space."

"Oh, that's fine. I'm not here to eat. I'm just waiting, actually," Hailey said.

"Oh? I saw the sign on the door that said they're hiring. Are you here for an interview?"

"Me? Oh, no. Actually, I am doing some volunteer work for the Chamber of Commerce. However, I *am* looking for work, as well," Hailey stated.

"What type of work are you looking for?" the woman asked.

"I have a marketing background, but I haven't had a lot of luck finding openings lately. I keep thinking tomorrow will be better, but that hasn't been the case. That's why I volunteered to work with the Chamber on the upcoming street fair. Have you heard about it?"

After hearing the details, the woman said, "It sounds like fun, but it looks like I'll be in Bali then."

"Nice!" Hailey said. "Enjoy your vacation!"

"I will, but it's not a vacation. I'm a coach, and I'm traveling to Indonesia to promote my new book," she informed.

"You wrote a book? What's it called?" Hailey asked.

"Creating Your Own Happiness," she answered.

Hailey's eyes darted to the book on the counter.

"That's your book right there? You're Yuri Choi?" she asked.

"Yes, it is, and I am," the woman smiled.

"I'm fascinated! Do you mind telling me how someone can create their own happiness? It seems as if I've struggled with that as of late," Hailey admitted.

"As a performance and fulfillment coach, I tell my clients that they have to fill their own cup," Yuri said, lifting her glass in demonstration. "You see, you need to come back to a place of self-love. It's only from a full cup that we can help ourselves and help others, as well"

"You're probably right. Lately, it seems that my cup is empty. At best, it gets half full, but then it runs back down again," Hailey sighed. "First, I went through a messy divorce, then I lost my job, and it hasn't gotten better since then."

"You're not alone. I've met many entrepreneurs and top performers who have felt the same way at some time. I've helped them uncover their blind spots to start living with purpose, aliveness, and passion, to live a more fulfilling life," Yuri advised.

"I recently talked to a man who told me I had to find my sweet spot and it was really quite enlightening. But, Yuri, how does one uncover their blind spot and start living that kind of life?" Hailey inquired.

"Well, the foundation of my book is to bring people back to the present moment, where they have the opportunity to create anything. In this moment, we can access who we are, and we are all creators. That's when we have infinite possibilities and start feeling alive and fulfilled," Yuri shared.

"It's not always easy to flip a switch and forget everything, though. I wish it was," Hailey replied wistfully.

"It's not a bad thing to acknowledge how we feel. Feelings are like colors—they aren't good or bad, positive or negative. They are what they are, and we should acknowledge them for what they are. But we can also acknowledge how we *want* to feel. When you do that, you set an intention for the way you want to feel, however that is. It's as easy as saying, 'I want to feel calm,' 'I want to feel happy.'"

Yuri paused for a moment to capture Hailey's response to her words. Seeing some uncertainty in her eyes, she continued.

"One thing I help my clients do is to change their stories and create experiences that change the energetic state in our bodies. Breathing exercises are great ways to do that. Take a moment to breathe and come back to the moment. In the present moment, there is no past or future. When you're in the present moment, you realize that you have an opportunity to create your day."

"Writing my book was a three-year labor of love. I've found along my journey and in my research with others that it's all about setting a goal and then being present in that journey. It doesn't matter where you are in that journey as long as you can stay present and know where you're headed," Yuri explained. "In that way, happiness is definitely an inside job."

Yuri explained that she initially was going to title her book, *Finding Your Own Happiness.* As she sat with it, she came to believe that it wasn't about "finding" happiness. Instead, it was about creating it.

"Think about it," she said, "finding happiness means that it exists and is waiting somewhere to be uncovered. Creating happiness, on the other hand, insinuates that happiness can be manmade. It can be invented at will."

"So, my glass really can be full?" Hailey asked.

"Yes, it can. Set a goal and be present. Above all, no matter where you are or what's going on in your life, know that it's all part of your unique journey," Yuri said.

At that moment, the hostess returned and informed Hailey that the owner was free to see her. "If you follow me, I'll take you back to her office."

"Of course," Hailey replied, before turning her attention back to Yuri.

"I really enjoyed our talk, and I promise to take your advice. The first chance I get, I'm going to order your book."

"Here, take mine," Yuri said, opening the front cover and jotting a note on the inside.

When Hailey opened it later to begin reading, she read the author's inscription, "Fill your cup with happy intentions. Your friend, Yuri."

CHAPTER SEVEN

T he following day, Hailey received the results of her assessment.

Her scores indicated that she was creative, collaborative, and people oriented. To her relief, marketing was listed as an optimal career for her, but so were vastly different careers, like event planner, business owner/manager, and journalist.

Wow, that's a diverse list, she thought. *But I do agree with the characteristics they identified. I've always enjoyed working with people and love being part of the pulse of a marketing campaign. Unfortunately, I wasn't afforded the opportunity to be creative and develop my own ideas at my previous job.*

Remembering that Yuri had said we are all creators, she wondered what she could do if she was given a chance to put her creativity to the test.

It wasn't long before she had an opportunity to find out.

The days had become warmer, and the sun's rays were springing nature back to life after being dormant over the winter. One day, Hailey noticed that the plant in her windowsill had grown significantly, but it had gotten so tall that it was drooping from its weight. On top of that, the single yellow bloom was arching toward the natural light on the other side of the windowpane. Realizing she needed to transplant it into a larger pot, she decided to make a quick trip to the store to find something suitable.

"Good morning, Ms. Hailey," greeted JB when she stepped out of the elevator.

"Hi, JB," she said, her face lighting up when she saw the friendly doorman. "Beautiful day, isn't it?"

"Well, yes, it most certainly is," JB replied, recognizing a change in Hailey's demeanor recently. "Are you having any luck on the job front?"

"Not just yet, but I have faith, JB," she said. "The Chamber is keeping me busy, too, so I feel productive. Besides, I've found that I really enjoy volunteering. It's a great way to introduce myself to neighboring businesses and residents. Oh, that reminds me, JB, do you know if our apartment complex is participating in the street festival next month?"

"I'm sure the tenants will be attending," JB said.

"No, not that—I mean is the apartment participating? Opening itself to the public? Offering anything special in front of the building?" she asked, pointing out the window.

"I don't think so. I guess it never occurred to me that we could do anything," he said. "After all, we're just an apartment building. We don't really have anything to offer to a street festival," he replied.

"Hmmm, well, there is some space on the walk outside these doors," she said. "Maybe we could figure something out with that space. JB, all of the businesses are doing *something*. The bistro will be giving free samples, as well as an outdoor truck. The bookstore has some local authors doing book signings, and the craft store is selling jewelry and demonstrating calligraphy techniques. Even the bank…"

"But what could we do, Ms. Hailey? What do you have in mind?" he asked.

"I don't know. It would be awesome if we could offer some live entertainment on our property, but there isn't much space in front," she said thoughtfully.

"And don't forget, tenants need to be able to come and go. We have them to consider … and the fire code," he reminded her.

"I know. It's too bad, though, that there isn't more space. You know, I wish I knew more of the tenants and could get their ideas," she said. "Oh, well, I'll think about it a bit more. For now, I've got to make a trip to the hardware store."

"Does something need repair in your apartment, Ms. Hailey? I can contact maintenance if you want," he said.

"Oh, no. Everything's fine—perfect, actually. I'm just looking for a flower pot. It's starting to look like I have a bit of a green thumb, and my only plant is growing wild trying to reach up to the sun through the window," she laughed. "You know, it's beautiful days like today that make me wish I had a little garden full of flowers. Wouldn't that be glorious?"

With that, Hailey walked out the door.

As soon as she was out the door, JB had an idea, and he quickly picked up the phone.

***

Inside the hardware store, she recognized the owner, who was talking to a man she didn't know. Acknowledging him with a quick smile and nod, she glanced up and down the aisles of the neighborhood store, trying to see where the garden products were located.

"Can I help you?" the owner said, pulling himself away from his conversation.

"I don't mean to disturb you. I was just looking for a new flowerpot, that's all," she replied.

"It's not a problem at all. Arjang and I were just catching up. Arjang, this is Ms. Hailey; she's been helping the Chamber of Commerce plan the street festival I was telling you about. Hailey, this is Arjang Zendehdel. He's a success and fulfillment coach and consultant, but also a good friend."

"Hello, it's very nice to meet you," Arjang said.

"Likewise. Please don't let me interrupt your conversation. This isn't urgent. I just thought I'd get a little transplanting done while the sun is still shining," Hailey apologized.

"Oh, but isn't the sun always shining?" Arjang asked.

"Pardon me?" Hailey asked, unsure what he was referring to.

"When it's night time, is the sun still shining? The answer is yes. When it's cloudy, is the sun still shining? The answer again is yes. The sun is always shining—we just can't see it when it's cloudy or the earth is rotating on its axis," he explained.

"You're right! That's a unique perspective," she commented.

"Well, it is what I teach my clients. Everyone has setbacks and bad days, but I use the sun metaphor to remind them that even though they can't see it at that moment, happiness is their true nature. It's true, Hailey. Our true selves are happy. That can get blocked by clouds of negative emotions and thoughts that keep us from seeing that light and experiencing it. Our light, peace, and power can get blocked by negativity, but it doesn't eliminate the light. It just covers it," Arjang said.

"I like that! It makes dark and dreary moments more bearable to know that the sun is right behind them. I have to say, it's coincidental to meet you, since I've been searching for answers in my own quest lately," Hailey said.

"And what are you searching for?" Arjang asked.

"I guess you could say I'm searching for the secret of happiness," Hailey replied.

"Well, that's something you cannot find, for it's already in you. You're born with it, actually. If babies are fed well and sleep well, they are naturally happy. If they're not, you say, 'What's wrong with the baby? There must be something wrong.' You see, we think it's normal when babies are happy and abnormal when they're crying."

"That's so true. I never thought of it like that," Hailey admitted.

"That's why I say that happiness is not something to pursue. It is something to uncover."

Given that statement, Hailey was interested in hearing what Arjang had to say about moments when things happen that affect our happiness.

"But what do we do when something interferes with that happiness, say a divorce or a losing a job?" she asked.

"That brings me to the two forms of happiness: conditional happiness and unconditional happiness. My focus in my field is unconditional happiness. You ask how someone can be happy regardless of the ups and downs of life? In my experience, anyone can be happy. Every human being has experienced happiness at some point in life. The real skill is determining how to be happy despite the ups and downs!"

"That's a skill I haven't developed," Hailey laughed.

"You can. When you connect to your true self, you are able to be happy, all the time. That doesn't mean that you don't have emotions. Even when I'm crying, my true self is happy. Even though that emotion is moving through me, I'm able to connect with my true self. I'm grounded with my true self, which is always stable, always a shining light. It's like the sun within, and it's never extinguished."

"Hailey, here's a little-known secret. Our emotions come from our thoughts, interpretations, and meanings, not from our circumstances. They do not come from what is happening—they come from how we interpret what is happening. It is how we interpret what is happening that makes us happy, angry, afraid, or whatever the emotion is. That is one of the most important pieces of information for any human being to know," Arjang explained.

Then he continued to explain.

"There are people who have plenty. They have family, love, fame, and wealth, but they've committed suicide. Then there are people who have very little, yet they are very happy. It's not what we have or how much we have; it's how we interpret those circumstances that leads to our emotions."

"That is our next secret, Hailey, which is it's important to manage how we interpret things and the meaning we give to them. It's how we see our reality through a lens and how we filter that reality. The fact that we are in a human body means that we experience things differently than other species. In addition, we are automatically filtering reality through our memories. We bring those memories into our current circumstances, and they invoke our responses. Fifty people can go through the same situation, and they can each have a different response, because they have a different filter and different memories," the success and fulfillment expert explained.

"Those filters you talk about, could they be something like seeing the world through rose-colored glasses?" Hailey asked.

"Absolutely! I think you get the idea. The filter you see things through is uniquely yours, but regardless, the sun is always shining, even though it's temporarily covered.

Just remember that happiness isn't a quest—it's not a game of hide and seek. It's in you. It always has been," he smiled encouragingly.

"Thank you. I've really enjoyed our talk and am glad I got the chance to meet you!" Hailey said. "Now, I better grab one of these flowerpots while I still have time to get out there and enjoy some of that sun!"

CHAPTER EIGHT

A s usual, JB greeted her upon her return.

"Ms. Hailey, if you have a minute, I'd like to show you something," he said.

"Of course, JB," she agreed.

"Come with me," he said as he opened a locked door and led her down a hallway to the back of the building. From there, he opened another door that took them outside.

Hailey's eyes grew wide as she gazed at the courtyard. She'd always known there was one at the back of the building, but it had never been appealing. If anything, it was barren and neglected, a brick patio that crossed the width of the entire building with a few benches on the edges. It wasn't a retreat, by any means. It didn't attract even the occasional guest or guests who wanted to enjoy a peaceful outdoor setting.

Today, however, the courtyard contained flats of bright flowers in vibrant shades of yellow, coral, and pink. Stacks of flower boxes and planters were neatly placed alongside a flower cart, which held gardening tools and several bags of potting soil.

"How pretty!" she said as she ran her fingers across the delicate blooms. "This is going to be such an improvement! When it's done, people will utilize this space. I know I will!"

"And it's all thanks to you," JB commented.

"Me?" she asked, confused.

"Earlier today, you mentioned wishing we had space where we could attract visitors or offer entertainment for events like the festival. It reminded me about this courtyard that is rarely utilized, so I made a few phone calls," he explained.

"And you were able to make all of this happen in such a short time?"

"Well, my wife's sister has a greenhouse just outside of town. I sent her a couple pictures of the courtyard, and she did the rest," he told her.

"Wait—please tell me that you didn't pay for all of this," Hailey said.

"Don't worry. I was able to get approval. As a matter of fact, management was very much in favor of it," he reported.

"That's awesome! I can't wait to see it when it's done! It's going to look amazing, JB. Do you think it will be ready before the festival? The sooner the flowers are planted, the sooner they'll grow and fill these beautiful planters."

"I can check on the timeframe," he answered.

Then Hailey had an idea.

"Hey, JB, do you think management would object if I did the planting? I used to help my grandmother with her flower garden, so I know what I'm doing. If they'd let me do it, I could have it done in a couple days," she said, unable to hide her excitement.

"Well, I don't think maintenance will object," JB smiled. "They let me pick out the flowers, so I don't see why they wouldn't let you do the gardening—that is if you really want to."

"Oh, I do! I can't wait to get started. To be honest, I'm so grateful to live here; it'll be my way of giving back! I just hope everyone else approves when I'm done."

"When they do, I'll make sure you get the credit. It was you who put the idea in my head."

"That brings me back to the reason I wished we had outdoor space," Hailey admitted.

"Yes, Ms. Hailey?"

"JB, I recently met a musician on the bus. His name is Weston, and he is awesome! The trouble is he's in a catch-22. He's not getting steady paying gigs because he doesn't have the exposure or following just yet, but he doesn't have the money to hire someone to create a website or professional demos. I tried to get him in the lineup for the festival, but there's a fee for that, too. That leaves getting permission to perform on private property, and this would be perfect. Now, how do I go about getting approval from management for Weston to perform back here?"

As he listened, JB was so impressed with Hailey's ideas and initiative that he set out to put her mind at ease.

"I tell you what, Ms. Hailey, you worry about transforming the courtyard, and I'll worry about the rest."

***

By the middle of the week, Hailey had completed her mission, and she couldn't wait to get JB's reaction.

It didn't disappoint. He was genuinely impressed.

"I can't believe how different it looks!" he said. "It's amazing what adding a few flowers and some colorful planters will do."

"A few flowers? There were 72 to be exact! Well, 73," she corrected herself, remembering that she had rehomed the flower on her windowsill to the courtyard. "I added a plant of my own. It looks so much happier here!"

"It all looks great. You did a fantastic job," JB complimented. "Now that you're done and the courtyard is fit for guests, I can tell you that management has given their approval to let your musician friend perform here during the festival. As a matter of fact, they asked me to submit an invoice so he could be paid."

"That's wonderful! I can't wait to tell Weston; he'll be so excited!" she exclaimed.

After admiring the courtyard for a few more minutes, JB unlocked the back door. When they walked through the doorway, Hailey stopped.

"JB, I've been meaning to ask—what is that? It looks like an elevator, but there aren't any buttons on the wall," she asked.

"It is an elevator, and you're right—there aren't any buttons. There is another one on the opposite side of the wall, too."

"Two elevators? What are they for? And why don't they have any buttons?"

"They're accessible by key only, and they lead to the top three floors of the building," he answered.

"What's up there? The front elevator only goes to the 15th floor."

"The 16th and 17th floors are currently unoccupied. Management is waiting to see what the needs are and how to best use that space, so they will be completed in phase two of the renovation. On the top floor, there is a private apartment and a few offices," he advised.

"An apartment on the top floor? Like a penthouse?" she grinned.

"I wouldn't say it's a penthouse suite, but I have to admit that it is nice," JB shared.

"Who lives there?"

"The manager of the building lives on the top floor, and his staff work in the offices up there, too."

"Wow, he lives here, and I've never seen him! You'd think he'd introduce himself, wouldn't you?" she wondered out loud. "I wonder why he hasn't."

"I don't know, Ms. Hailey, but I'm sure he has his reasons," mentioned JB.

***

After their conversation, Hailey was on a crusade. She talked to Weston, who gladly accepted the opportunity to perform during the festival. Now, all she had to do was get the word out to the rest of the tenants. She wanted to "pack the courtyard" for his concert.

She also wanted to find out if the tenants had any suggestions or ideas for the two empty floors. Hoping to reach out to as many tenants as possible, JB suggested she put a notice on the bulletin board in the mailroom. He also reminded her that the apartment's app had a forum where she could spark the conversation.

At the same time, there was so much to do in the final push before the festival that she realized she hadn't thought about anything else, including being divorced and unemployed.

I guess I'm filling my own cup, she thought.

Still, when one of the tenants reached out to her in response to the notice she posted, she was happy to make time to meet with her. Hailey was happy to suggest that they meet in the courtyard.

From the moment they met, she felt like Nicole Vignola was a friend.

She discovered that Nicole was a neuroscientist and health expert, but she was also so easy to talk to.

"I'm just like everyone else. In my job, I need to stay professional, but I'm like you. I love summer days and going to festivals, too," Nicole said.

"Neuroscience can sound intimidating, but it's also fascinating," Hailey remarked.

"It is fascinating to me. I really want to make neuroscience relevant to everyday life. It is really important to our health and fitness, and especially our happiness," she shared.

"So, tell me exactly what you do," invited Hailey.

"The short version is that I use science-based evidence to empower people with the tools they need to optimize their overall wellbeing. Only then can they live their optimal life," explained Nicole.

"Do you believe that we have the ability to determine our own level of happiness?" Hailey asked.

"Happiness, in my opinion, is having a good relationship with yourself, physically, emotionally, and mentally. They're all integrated," Nicole explained. "And it all starts at the cellular level."

"Does that mean we can't change it?"

"Not at all. We know that our cells regenerate, and what we put into our bodies affects the output. I always say that acknowledgement and knowledge are the first step. If you know you want to change something and are aware of it, you've already planted the seed."

"So, if I want to be healthier or happier, I need to acknowledge that fact, and the seed will begin to grow?"

"That's step one. Visualization is also important. See yourself the way you want to be. The brain can't tell the difference between reality and thoughts. That's how important your thoughts are. For instance, if you can think about how you are going to execute your day, your brain starts to integrate a pattern of neuronal firing that is sequenced for you to do what you've told it. The same thing goes for negative thought patterns. The brain only knows what you repeat to it over and over, and it will integrate those patterns. So whatever you are repeating is what you will become," Nicole said.

"Okay. So, let's say I'm down and feeling negative. How can I change that?" Hailey asked.

"Every time you are aware that you have those feelings, interrupt that thought pattern with something else. Our thoughts change the way we feel, which can then change the way we act, which can then influence our thoughts. It's a pattern that repeats itself."

"Use the negative to remind you of the positive. So many of our behaviors are automatic; it's the way our brains operate. But we can use that negative thing as a trigger to break the habit of that thought. Like I said, it requires both attention and intention," Nicole continued. "Some things are so deeply ingrained in our behavior and thoughts that we may not even be aware of them. However, the brain likes what it knows. You might not like being unhappy and negative, but that's what your brain knows, so that's the pattern it will continue to execute because it's easy to do what it knows. On the other hand, if you plant the seed that you want to be happy, you'll subconsciously do everything to get to that goal."

"Oh, my goodness, I love this. Because I've been struggling after going through a divorce and losing my job. I really needed to hear this," Hailey said.

"Things like relationships and careers give us a sense of connection, Hailey, but it's been proven that you don't need those things to have connections. Connection comes down to nature, who you are, and your values. Maybe you saw yourself as a wife and an employee, but who are you without your marriage or your job? Those things are external. If you know who you are outside of those roles, you'll know what makes you happy," Nicole advised.

"I think I'm beginning to discover that, Nicole. For the first time, I have nothing to worry about but me," Hailey mentioned, before laughing and adding, "and the festival, and this courtyard, and now spearheading phase two of our apartment's renovation project."

Laughing, Nicole said, "Look at us—we've been talking and totally forgot the reason I reached out to you!"

"You're right! So, let me ask, Nicole, do you have any ideas about what they should do with the two empty floors? I'd love to hear them!"

"As a matter of fact, I do. Wouldn't it be great if they turned one of the floors into a fitness center? What an awesome benefit it would be if we had a place to change our health and wellness! It would empower all of the tenants to optimize their overall wellbeing and do wonders for our emotional and mental health," Nicole suggested.

"I love it, especially since I had to give up my gym membership when I lost my job. Let's make a laundry list of what we'd like it to look like," Hailey said.

"That's a plan. If we visualize it, our brains are going to start working to make it happen," Nicole reminded her.

CHAPTER NINE

Hailey woke up early on the day of the festival and quickly checked the weather forecast. She braced herself, as the evening before, the weather had called for a chance of rain. To her relief, the sun gods were shining down on her that day.

After getting dressed, she put on her most comfortable walking shoes, making sure she was prepared to be on her feet most of the day.

Then she slung a backpack over her shoulders and hustled down the hall.

"Good morning, JB!" she said when the elevator door opened.

"Well, aren't you bright and cheery this morning! And it looks like Mother Nature is going to cooperate with your plans," JB smiled.

"I know. I've been so excited for today. The last thing we need is rain!"

"I'm sure everything will be perfect, Ms. Hailey. You've worked hard. Now, relax and enjoy it," JB suggested.

"Thanks, JB. I hope you're right! See you later!" she said as she bolted out the door.

She spent the next couple hours strolling down the blocks, making sure vendors had what they needed, and answering questions. Along the way, she admired the creative booths, business displays and the occasional mouthwatering scents coming from the food trucks strategically placed along the festival's path.

She had just passed a couple teenage employees who were joking with each other as they set up a red and white checkered table outside of the pizza place. She was still smiling at their carefree camaraderie when she past the bookstore, where three people were in various phases of stacking books, lining up pens, and preparing for their book signings.

She was so preoccupied with other thoughts that it didn't register what she saw until she past it.

Wait—what? I must be seeing things, she thought, as she walked back to the last table.

And to her surprise, her eyes hadn't deceived her. Hailey thought she gasped out loud when she read the book cover: *Happy for No Reason.*

More than a little curious, Hailey picked the book up. She just had to know what the book was about and who had written it.

The bio on the inside flap read,

"An authority on happiness, Marci Shimoff is a world-renowned transformation teacher on happiness success and a *New York Times* bestselling author of two books, "Happy for No Reason" and "Love for No Reason.""

"Can I help you?"

Hailey looked up to the smiling face of the same woman whose photograph was on the back cover.

"Oh, hi! I'm sorry—when I saw the title of your book, I just had to pick it up and see what it's about. Happy for No Reason! How did you come up with that title?" she asked.

"Being happy for no reason means that your happiness doesn't depend on anything or anyone else. As soon as your happiness depends on something, your ability to be happy is out of your control," she explained.

"There are two kinds of happiness," Marci explained. "First, there is happy for a good reason. In other words, everything is working in your life. The bills are paid. Your relationships are great. You're doing great work and gaining recognition. That is conditional happiness. Then there is happy for no reason, which is unconditional happiness. That is lasting happiness, and all that we really want," she shared.

"Marci, if I read your book, what will I learn? What's your secret to happiness…"

Without a hint of hesitation, Marci graced her with an answer.

"I can tell you that right now. It is knowing that you are the divine, that you are love and light. It is feeling and knowing that in every cell of your body that you are a miracle. Being happy for no reason means that you have an inner state of peace and wellbeing that doesn't depend on your circumstances, whether things are great or not always great. That doesn't mean that you'll smile at all times, but it does mean that no matter what is going on, you're happy inside," she said.

"It just seems like being happy is the one universal thing that everyone wants, including me. You'd think there would be a universal secret to attaining it," Hailey said.

"Happiness is the goal of all goals. It's why people want a better job, more money, or relationships, for they believe those things will bring them more happiness," Marci shared. "But if fame, success, and looks were the key to happiness, we'd see a lot more happy people in Hollywood," she quipped.

"Now to answer your question about the best way to attain happiness, it's safe to say that everything around us either contributes to our pursuit of happiness or it takes away from it. The definition of real lasting and authentic happiness is the inner state of peace and wellbeing that you bring with you. It's not about extracting happiness *from* your life circumstances. It's about bringing happiness *to* your life circumstances," informed Marci.

"The fact that happiness seems to be fleeting or out of arm's reach might be because we live in a society where there are two prevalent myths: I'll be happy when …

when I have enough money, when I fall in love, when my family is complete, when I buy my dream home, when I retire.

"Then there's the myth of more. You got what you wanted and were happy, but then that happiness waned, and you find you need more of whatever that was to become happy again."

"I'm following you. Actually, I am starting to see where I fit into those myths," Hailey smiled.

"Well, happiness is more than a myth. There is actual science that backs it. Science shows that we each have a happiness set point. It's like a thermostat. No matter what happens to us, whether it's good or bad, we will hover around our thermostat setting, unless we do something consciously to change it."

"That's interesting. How do we determine our happiness set point?" Hailey asked.

"That's a good question. It is 50 percent genetic. You are born with that. It's ten percent our circumstances. That is such a tiny piece of the pie, yet most of the people in the world are chasing those circumstances to try to be happier. The other 40 percent is based on our habits, thoughts, and behavior," she advised.

"Scientists in the field of epigenetics say that when we change our habits, our DNA is influenced. That means that 90 percent of our happiness set point can be changed by changing our habits," she said.

"That's similar to what a neuroscientist recently told me," Hailey mentioned.

"It's true. And here's another truth: the only difference between happy people and everybody else is that they have different habits," Marci disclosed. "One of those habits is the way we think."

Then pausing, Marci said, "I'm sorry. This is my passion. I could talk about it all day. I don't mean to keep you."

"Oh, no, no, no. You're not keeping me. The title of your book really speaks to me. Believe me, I'm captivated by our conversation. Please, continue," Hailey encouraged the author.

"Okay, I'll give you the condensed version. Scientists say that the average person has 60,000 thoughts a day. For the average person, 80 percent of those thoughts are negative. It's called the negativity bias. We inherited it from our ancestors, who needed to remember the negative in order to survive. We no longer need that, but we are stuck. That is called the Velcro-Teflon syndrome. Our minds are like

Velcro for the negative, it just sticks to us, but they are like Teflon for the positive. I've seen that happy people reverse that tendency and become Velcro for the positive and Teflon for the negative.

"Here's an example: you get 10 compliments a day and one criticism. At the end of the day, most people remember that criticism, while happy people remember the positive compliments. They don't turn a blind eye to the criticism, but they build neuropathways in the brain for the positive."

Marci then shared what she calls The House of Happiness, which consists of 21 main happiness habits that fall into seven categories. She explained them each briefly.

"The foundation. The foundation is taking responsibility for your life and happiness. If you show up as a victim and blame others, you'll never be happy. On the other hand, if you are accountable for your own happiness, you'll ask yourself what you can do to change it.

"Second is the pillar of the mind: These are your thoughts and, again, focusing on positive thoughts is a habit that supports happiness.

"Next is the pillar of the heart: how open hearted are you? Do you live with joy, gratitude, kindness, generosity, and forgiveness? Positive heart habits will influence happiness," she said.

"Then, there is the pillar of the body: Do you have the biochemistry for happiness? Endorphins are happiness hormones, and dopamine makes us feel excited and stimulated!

"After that, comes the soul: Do you feel a deep connection to the energy of the universe?

"And then there is the roof: This is your purpose and passion. What inspires you and makes you want to get out of bed in the morning? The roof of your house of happiness is living a life that incorporates your purpose and gifts. This produces life satisfaction and, of course, the ability to be happy.

"Last, but not least, there is the garden: Do you have a lot of weeds (people) who are dragging you down, or are you surrounded with roses and gardenias?"

"Marci, I'm happy to say that lately I've been surrounded by the most beautiful flowers of every shape and color," Hailey admitted proudly.

"Enjoy them! Often, I see people who don't believe they deserve to be happy. In fact, the number one question I'm asked is, 'Is it selfish to want to be happy?' My response is that being happy is the least selfish thing you can do because it is contagious. Just as negativity can drag you down, happiness can build others up. When you're happy, you spread happiness to everyone you come into contact with. When you make yourself happy, you then have the ability to change the world by making others happy—one person at a time," she said.

"I'm just beginning to realize that, Marci. But it reminds me that it will probably make a lot of people happy if I get back to work!" Hailey laughed. "But not before I buy your book! And I'd love it if you'd sign it for me."

When they were done, Hailey walked away, book in arm and a skip in her step. She didn't even realize that everyone who saw her could read her like a book.

They all could see that she was happy for no reason.

CHAPTER TEN

It was an extremely busy day, but it sped by too fast.

Before Hailey knew it, it was 5:00, which was her signal to get back to the apartment building. Weston was slated to play at 6:00, and she wanted to be there to make sure he had everything he needed.

As she entered the courtyard, she was pleased to see that it had already attracted several guests, even an hour before the show started.

Catching a glimpse of Weston, she walked straight to him.

"Welcome!" she said.

"Hi, Hailey! Hey, this place looks great. I'm excited to get started," he said.

"Thanks. Is there anything I can do? Do you need an extension cord, a chair, should I move anything?"

"I don't need a thing. Relax, everything's perfect," he assured her. "Why don't you sit down for a few minutes while I get tuned up?"

"That sounds like a good idea. I've been on my feet since this morning," Hailey admitted as she turned around to claim a chair. Eyeing a table occupied by a man and a woman, she asked if they minded if she joined them for a few minutes.

"Please do," the woman said. "We're just waiting for Weston to get started."

"You know him?" Hailey asked.

"Yes. Actually, I worked downtown, where I was privileged to hear Weston play. It was always something I looked forward to," said.

Just then, Weston approached their table.

"Hailey, I want you to meet Michelle Patterson, the CEO of Women Network LLC. Michelle is also an author, visionary, speaker, and a talk show host. I've known her for several years now, and when you told me I got this gig, she was the first person I called."

Laughing, Michelle said, "I always told him when he became famous, I'd be his biggest fan."

As Weston walked away, Michelle asked, "Are you the Hailey that he's so grateful to, for doing all of this for him?"

"Well, yes, but I really didn't do much."

"To Weston, you did. You took a chance and did something to help a stranger. You didn't have to do that. But I'm glad you did. You see, singing is his passion. He'd rather do it for free than do anything else for money. Through it all, he's never lost faith. It's about time he got some recognition for his talent, and I thank you for that," Michelle said.

Michelle's sincerity quickly warmed Hailey's heart. As they talked, Michelle introduced her to her husband, and they settled into a pleasant conversation.

It wasn't long before Michelle shared that she had been diagnosed with stage four breast cancer.

"That diagnosis transformed my life," Michelle shared. "This journey has been an opportunity for me to sit back and receive. I have never felt as much unconditional love as I have in the last few years. It has given me an opportunity to have conversations and dialogue with my family that I've never had. It's been amazing and like nothing I have ever experienced."

"What an incredible outlook! Most people wouldn't be able to express a positive perspective of such a diagnosis," Hailey commented.

"It's made me look at myself and my life differently. It's also shown me the things that are most important in my life. I used to think my career made me happy. I used to believe that awards and being on stage with celebrities in front of huge audiences made me happy. But that's because I didn't yet know what happiness is all about," Michelle explained.

"What is it about, Michelle?" Hailey asked softly.

"To me, the secret of happiness is unconditional love. It's being raw and fully open. There have been tough moments, and through it all, it has been overwhelming to feel the unconditional love as my family has cared for me.

"My old definition of happiness was being in the spotlight, enjoying fame and connecting with a large number of people. I didn't realize, though, that I was disconnected with my family. It's interesting that where I am in life right now, there are no awards or other things that used to matter to me. I've given myself permission to let myself matter to me. The day I was diagnosed, my husband told me that I needed to treat myself like somebody I'm responsible for taking care of. He reminded me that I needed to be mama bear for me. That is when I started to own my wellness," she shared.

Hailey glanced toward Michelle's husband in admiration for the advice he'd given his wife. Smiling, he reached out and held Michelle's hand as she continued to share her story.

"When I was told that my cancer had metastasized and was everywhere, my response was, 'So you think I have a chance?!' While some might think that this wasn't a good time to make a joke, I say it was the best time to be making jokes.

"I had to learn what was best for me, my health, and my happiness. And that's just what I did. My house is now set up as a healing home. No negativity is allowed. There is even a sign at the door that unapologetically says, 'Leave your shoes and your ego at the door.'"

"I love that!" Hailey exclaimed her approval.

"I discovered that I had to let go of my ego. I learned that it's okay to cry, to be afraid, and to let myself be loved. I also learned that it's okay to love myself, unconditionally and unapologetically. I have to do that to own my wellness."

"I admire your attitude, Michelle," Hailey said. "If you hadn't told me, I wouldn't have known you had cancer. You look so content, so happy."

"When I was diagnosed, I was told I had 90 days to live! Three years later, I am living a life full of loving moments. Before my diagnosis, I wasn't 100 percent loving myself. Through my journey, though, I have become my own best friend. I am now authentic and love myself completely. When I showed up to love myself, it transformed my interactions with others. My home has become so loving, and as my family loves me, it has been amazing to reciprocate that unconditional love," she shared. "I find it gives me more love to share with others, like Weston and people like him who make me happy, too."

As if on cue, Weston stepped up to the microphone and introduced himself to the audience.

For the next hour, he captivated the crowd as they got caught up in his music. The musician had a knack for relating to the audience and making them feel as if they were a part of the music. Before long, they were singing along to the tunes and dancing to the beat.

Rounding out his set, he finished with the crowd favorite, 'Sweet Caroline', followed by 'Build Me Up', Buttercup'. By this time, the audience had grown, and the sing-along could be heard a block away.

Hailey watched his performance, from start to finish, with Michelle and her husband. Just like she had on the bus, she found herself singing along, and when she looked to her side, she saw that Michelle had joined in and was enjoying every minute.

At that moment, Hailey had every reason to be happy ... for no reason.

***

When the night was over and the goodbyes said, Hailey thanked JB for everything.

"Weston's show was great, and I'm grateful for everything you did to make it happen," she said.

"I enjoyed it very much! I have a feeling that young man isn't going to be a stranger around here. He gained quite a few new fans tonight," JB noticed.

"I think you're right. It was a great day—a perfect day. And I couldn't be happier," Hailey declared. "Strange, isn't it? I still don't have a job. I don't have a husband, but I *am* happier than I've been in a long time! I wonder why."

"That's easy. Ms. Hailey, once you know what makes you happy, you can choose to be happy all the time. It seems to me that you've found what makes you happy. And I believe that is the true universal secret of happiness. You see, happiness is different for everybody. For some, it's sunshine and roses. For others, it's dancing in the rain. For some, it's waking up healthy. For those who are ill, it might be unconditional love and acceptance of what they do have. You and only you can own your happiness, and that's not a secret. It's an age-old truth, and I live by it every day."

"So, you're telling me there is no one secret of happiness, after all?" she asked.

"That's right. But there is one secret that I have been keeping, and I think it's time to divulge the truth," JB said.

"What's that?"

"Let me start by saying that I've watched you grow in the last few months, Hailey, and I want you to know that you've impressed me. I'm going to miss seeing you every day."

"What do you mean? I'm not going anywhere—not yet, anyway," she asked.

"I have a feeling you're not going anywhere for a long time. I'm the one who is leaving," he announced.

"What? You're leaving? Management is letting you leave? They should give you a huge raise to stay!" she exclaimed. "You've become a part of this building. It won't be the same without you!"

Smiling, JB said, "Let me share a story with you. I love this building and have for as long as I can remember. My parents got an apartment in this building when they got married, before they started a family and moved to a two-story house out in the suburbs. When I learned that the city was planning to level this building and replace it with a parking lot, I knew I couldn't let that happen and immediately made them an offer they couldn't resist."

After a brief pause to see if Hailey was following him, JB shared his secret.

"That's right. My name isn't actually JB; it's Jackson Barrett."

"Jackson Barrett as in Jackson Barrett Enterprises?"

"One and the same. I own this building, and I've also been the manager. My wife and I lived on the top floor—that is, until today. You see, when the renovations were finished, I knew how much this building meant, not only to my family, but to the community. I wanted to make sure its history was preserved, while it was also appreciated by someone who had the same vision as me. So, I decided to manage the building myself until I could find that person," JB said.

"And you have found that person?" Hailey asked, still having difficulty believing what JB had told her.

"I believe I have," he said, handing her a ring of keys. "Hailey, I didn't want this building for myself. I just wanted to make sure its beauty and significance in the community would always be here for others. As I've watched you throughout the last several months, I've become confident that you are the manager I've been looking for. Here are the keys to your new apartment. Maintenance will be available to help you in the morning."

"The keys to the top floor?"

"That's right. The penthouse suite," he grinned.

"JB, uh Jackson, I mean Mr. Barrett, I can't thank you enough! I do love this building, and I will take fantastic care of it!"

"You can call me Jackson," he smiled. "I think we're going to be working together for a long time."

"I hope so," Hailey said. "But before you go, can I ask you a question?"

"Of course. What is it?"

"What is *your* secret to happiness?"

He didn't have to think about how to reply to her question. Without hesitation, he stated his answer.

"Making other people happy," he said, "but that's not a secret anymore, is it?"

GREG S. REID

For over 25 years, Greg has inspired millions of people to take personal responsibility to step into the potential of their greatness and, as such, his life of contribution has been recognized by government leaders, a foreign Princess, as well as luminaries in education, business, and industry.

Mr. Reid has been published in over 150 books, including 38 bestsellers in 45 languages. Titles such as Stickability: The Power of Perseverance; The Millionaire Mentor, and Three Feet from Gold: Turn Your Obstacles into Opportunities have inspired countless readers to understand that the most valuable lessons we learn are also the easiest ones to apply.

Greg Reid is known best for being Founder of Secret Knock, a Forbes and Inc. Magazine top-rated event focused on partnership, networking, and business development.

He is the producer of the Oscar-qualified film, Wish Man, based on the creator of the Make A Wish Foundation, which is now streaming globally.

For his work in mentoring youth in his hometown of San Diego, Mr. Reid was honored by the White House, where a former President commended Greg for his work for positively working with youth through a local mentorship program.

And if that is not enough, recently Greg was awarded an honorary PhD in literature and a star on the infamous Las Vegas Walk of Stars.

Made in the USA
Columbia, SC
13 February 2024

31425679R00065